It's a
mystery
to me, Lord

From the Best-Selling Series
young readers
More than one million sold!

It's a mystery to me, Lord

Bible devotions and activities for boys

David Allen Sorensen

Augsburg
MINNEAPOLIS

IT'S A MYSTERY TO ME, LORD
Bible Devotions and Activities for Boys

Scripture quotations unless otherwise noted are from Today's English Version of the Bible, copyright 1976, American Bible Society, and are used by permission.

Photos courtesy of Images © 1995 PhotoDisc, Inc., cover; Barbara Brockmann, p. 8; Bob Taylor, p. 16; Jim Cronk, p. 38; Jean-Claude Lejeune, p. 44; Renaud Thomas, p. 48; Religious News Service, p. 54; Gene Plaisted, p. 60; Strix Pix, pp. 74, 78; Paul M. Schrock, p. 84; Florence Sharp, p. 96.

Cover design by Craig P. Claeys

Library of Congress Cataloging-in-Publication Data

Sorensen, David Allen, 1953–
  It's a Mystery to Me, Lord.

  Summary: In a series of stories, four boys encounter mysteries or questions about the demonstration of Christian principles in daily life, and their friend Mrs. Gratz helps them find solutions through Bible verses. Includes prayers and suggested activities.
  1. Boys—Religious life—Juvenile literature.
[1. Christian life. 2. Conduct of life] I. Title.
BV4541.2.S67   1985   248.8'2   85-22993
ISBN 0-8066-2183-4

The paper used in this publication meets the minimum requirements of American National Standard for Information Sciences—Permanence of Paper for Printed Library Materials, ANSI Z329.48-1984. ∞

Manufactured in the U.S.A. AF 9-2183

00   99   98   97   96   6   7   8   9   10   11   12   13   14

For Barbara,
my companion in exploring
the many mysteries

Contents

The Mystery Begins

"Here we are," Erik whispered in the dark. "Keep your heads down." He bent over and tip-toed quickly along the thorny hedge toward an enormous dark house. Three similar shapes stumbled behind him under the weight of an old wooden extension ladder. They all stopped at the end of the bushes.

"I don't see a light," Specs said.

"I told you it would be in back," Erik replied.

"I'm not so sure we should be doing this," Peter said. "Isn't this against the law?"

"We're not actually going *inside* the house," Erik said. "We just want to take a peek at what makes that eerie green light at night."

"Well, *I'm* not scared," Brian said. "Old Lady Gratz is probably asleep anyway."

"Unless that green light is her crystal ball," Erik said with a straight face, "in which case she is probably watching us right now."

"Is that what you think it is?" Peter asked. "Gee!"

"Come on, Pete," Specs said. "He's pulling your leg again."

"We'll see," Erik said. "Follow me, and don't make any noise!"

One by one they stepped through the gap between the bushes and the front gate, hauling the ladder with them. They rounded the old mansion at a dog-trot, finding their way clearly under the full moon. Turning the final corner, the three with the ladder almost ran into Erik. He had a finger to his lips and an arm stretched up and out. No words were necessary. In a second floor window, halfway across the back wall, a pale green light flickered mysteriously.

In almost total silence, the four boys laid the ladder on the grass and extended it as far as it would go. Then they lifted it to its full height and leaned it with a small thump against the house. Erik waited for nothing. He climbed swiftly to the top while the three others held the ladder steady. He peered for a moment into the window, then shuffled quickly down.

"She's there!" he hissed. "She's huddled over a round glass that gives off this weird green light."

"Let's get out of here," Peter said.

"He's pulling your leg again," Specs said. "Stop that, Erik."

"I'm not kidding!" he said, emphasizing every word.

"Well, *I'm* not scared," said Brian, as he clattered up the rickety ladder.

"Shhh . . . !" the boys signaled from below.

"There's nobody in the room," Brian said too loudly from above.

"What!" exclaimed Erik.

Suddenly, five huge bulbs lining the roof flashed on, one of them almost in Brian's face. This time, he *was* scared. He jerked back and began to climb down two rungs at a time. As the ladder teetered and fell, the others tried to catch him, but they all ended up in a heap.

For a moment, all was silent, then . . .

"Now that I have seen all your faces in the light, why don't you come in for some milk and cookies—or I'll call the police."

The boys looked up at Old Lady Gratz standing in the doorway, then at each other.

"Really, boys," she said firmly, "I insist!"

"So you came to solve a mystery," Mrs. Gratz said after they had eaten their fill of cookies and milk by candlelight. "Then you haven't fulfilled your task yet, have you?"

"We really should be going," Peter said.

"I guess if you're still scared—" she began.

"Well, *I'm* not scared," Brian said quickly.

"Of course you're not," she said, "but do you think you are brave enough to come upstairs and see the most mysterious thing in the house?"

11

"We really *should* be going," Peter said again, this time to Brian.

"Sure," Brian said. "Let's go see this mystery."

Of course, the others had no choice but to go along. None of them wanted this terrific story—sure to be told in school the next day—to end by calling them chickens.

Up the long, sweeping staircase they went, led by the mysterious woman carrying a single candle. Outside, the wind had picked up, making a number of the wooden shingles on the roof sound like willow whistles. They moved halfway down the long hall and stopped at a door on the left.

"Here we are," Mrs. Gratz said. "Our mystery room. You may enter."

Everything about the room was old. Old furniture, an old round rug covering the floor, an old tick-tocking grandfather's clock, and shelf after shelf of old, dark books smelling like someone's damp basement.

"See," said Erik, pointing, "there's that round glass with the green light, just as I said."

"It's my reading light," Mrs. Gratz said. "It's all I use these days in order to save electricity. Besides, this little oil lamp is the very lamp that my own grandmother used when she was a girl."

"But why does it give off a green glow?" Specs asked.

"Some old glass changes color over the years if it stands in the sunlight. Most will turn blue; this one turned green."

"So that is the mystery," Erik said.

"Partly," Mrs. Gratz said, "but I brought you up here for a different reason."

Peter started backing toward the door.

"I brought you here to show you something much older than this lamp; indeed, some of it is 850 generations old!"

She aimed a slender finger at a small stand near the lamp. On it was the most enormous book any of the boys had ever seen.

"Behold my greatest mystery, the treasure of this mansion, the light of my heart." Her voice had dropped almost to a whisper. *"It is the Word of God."*

Mrs. Gratz seemed to be waiting to see what effect her words would have on the boys.

Finally, Erik said, "I don't get it. It's a Bible, isn't it?"

"Is that all you see?" Mrs. Gratz asked with a kind smile. "Look closer."

The boys hesitated, then moved over to examine the Bible. Except for Peter, that is, who stayed at the door with one hand on the knob.

"What do you see?" Mrs. Gratz asked. "Old words on yellowed paper?" She chuckled to herself and her eyes looked merry. "Look closer yet."

They looked.

"I still don't get it," Erik said.

"When you get a letter from someone, do you see only paper and ink? Of course not. You have a picture of the person who wrote it in your mind's eye, don't you? But more than that, when they describe an experience to you, you can almost feel what they felt as they were going through it."

"And your Bible is like that?" Peter asked in a small voice from the doorway.

She whirled around and said, "Yes!" causing Peter to jump. "Once, Jesus appeared from *nowhere* to explain the Scriptures to two of his disciples, how the Savior had to suffer first before coming into his glory." Mrs. Gratz began walking toward Peter who now regretted that he had even opened his mouth. She continued, "And do you know what they said to each other when they finally realized that it was the Lord himself who had talked with them?"

"No," Peter squeaked.

"They said, 'Wasn't it like a *fire* burning in us. . . .' "

Peter heard the word *fire*, saw Mrs. Gratz almost upon him, and lost what small nerve he had mustered. He yelled once and yanked on the doorknob, only to find the smooth brass object come off in his hand. As he fumbled to reattach it, a hand grabbed his shoulder and pulled him around with surprising strength.

It was Brian.

"Show a little respect, Peter," Brian said under his breath.

"Never mind, son," Mrs. Gratz said, taking the knob. "We all are most afraid of the things we don't understand. But I have a proposal for you

14

all. A way that you can investigate and come to understand many things."

"Really? Like what?" Specs asked.

"How many real, mysterious, haunted houses are you boys likely to run across in this town?" Mrs. Gratz asked.

"Not many, I guess," Erik answered. "None, really."

"But life is full of mysteries—things that make you more than a little curious. Right?"

"Sure," Erik said.

"Well, I'll pit my Bible against any mysteries that you can bring me," Mrs. Gratz said. She looked from one face to another. "I think there are enough clues in this book that, together, we can explore almost anything."

She paused.

The boys looked at each other for a moment. Peter was shaking his head slightly, but none of the boys spoke up.

"I don't suppose you boys are afraid to come back here again," Mrs. Gratz said casually.

"*I'm* not scared," Brian said.

"I'm with him," Erik said.

"Here we go again," Specs said with a smile.

"Oh, dear," said Peter as he slumped against the door.

"Good," Mrs. Gratz said happily. "Come any-time, boys. Bring your mysteries—but next time leave your ladder at home."

Rumors of Riches

Mrs. Gratz had said "Come anytime, boys." "Anytime" ended up being the very next day.

The four friends had found their story to be a big hit at school. But it had gone through some changes in the telling. Peter left out the parts where he had been scared, Brian didn't bother to mention that he had fallen off the ladder, and "Old Lady Gratz" came off sounding more scary than she really was. Still, they mostly told the story as it happened—except that they all refused to name what had been so mysterious in the upper room. They referred to it as "The Great Treasure," and said things like "You wouldn't believe me if I told you" and "We'll be going back to learn its secrets" and such. But they didn't tell a single person that Mrs. Gratz's treasure was her old Bible. They thought it would spoil the story.

Soon, the whole school was buzzing about Old Lady Gratz's wealth. "Jewels in a chest," some said. "Money buried in the backyard in cans," said others. And everybody wanted to know about the treasure on the second floor. "What are they hiding?" everyone asked.

After school, Erik, Brian, Specs, and Peter headed once again toward the old mansion. Three times on their way there, kids rode up on bikes and asked if they were really going back there. "Just watch," Erik said for them all.

They arrived at the house and found three or four groups of kids trying to look like they were not there to gawk. But as the boys strolled right up to the front door and rang the bell, they did just that. Gawk.

"Come in, boys," Mrs. Gratz said from behind the screen door. "We'll go right up to the Reading Room."

The staircase was brighter, Peter was glad to see, and the upstairs hallway looked almost cheery in the daylight.

"So," she began, "here we are so soon again in my mystery room. I'm glad. Sit down." They sat.

Silence. The boys began to fidget.

"Where do we begin?" Mrs. Gratz asked. "What is our first mystery?" She waited for almost a minute, then said, "I know. You are here because your friends outside expect you to be here. Correct?"

"I guess we don't exactly have a mystery for you today," Brian said.

"You don't have to come up with a mystery for my sake," she replied. "You will find mysteries for yourselves."

"What do you mean?" Specs asked.

"If you go through life with sharp eyes and a clear mind, you will find things that you do not understand. Then bring them to me and I'll help you to find some Bible clues to help you in understanding them. Or better yet, explore the Bible on your own."

The boys fell silent again.

"That's all right. You go now until you have found your first mystery." She smiled and motioned to the door.

The boys rose to their feet and started to leave until Erik stopped and said, "I have it." The others turned to look at him. "The first mystery is you."

"Me?" Mrs. Gratz asked. "Why me?"

"People say all kinds of things about you, but I don't think anyone *really* knows."

"Knows what?"

"Like, if you are really rich or not."

Mrs. Gratz's fingers wiggled 10 different ways when she laughed. "Well," she said, "that one is easy enough." She grabbed her pointy glasses from the chain around her neck and put them on. Then she reached down and thumbed through the old Bible. She stopped three times, read silently, then wrote on a pad what book, chapter, and verse of the Bible she was reading.

Then she handed Erik the piece of paper. It said:

"*Bible Clues:* Matthew 6:19-21; Ecclesiastes 5:19; and Proverbs 22:1-2."

Action idea: Do you get an allowance? Do you sometimes get money as a gift? Figure out on paper where you usually spend your money or what you do with it. Do you give any of your money to church? Why or why not? Based on her Bible clues, do you think Mrs. Gratz is rich like all the rumors say?

Prayer time: Lord Jesus, money seems like a good thing, but I have to admit that it is possible to have a lot of it and still not be rich in the most important way. Thank you for depositing faith, hope, and love in my spiritual bank account. Help me to spend it all wisely. Amen.

A Weakling on the Team

"Hey guys! Look at Darrel's glove."

"Darrel, are you going to wear that or use it for third base?"

Specs walked up to his school buddies and said, "Come on guys, give him a break, OK?"

Specs liked Darrel. They were both quiet, they were both good in art, they were still shy around girls, and they were both tall and skinny. Specs liked Darrel because they were so much alike.

But they were different in many ways, too. Specs was from town; Darrel lived on a farm. Specs went out for every sport he could; Darrel always had to go home after school for chores. Specs had his group of friends; Darrel was a loner.

One of the boys kept up the teasing. "Take off your limp-noodle glove and try a he-man's glove," he said. "When I catch a real burner in this first baseman's mitt, it sounds like a stick of dynamite going off."

"It's very nice, Steve," Darrel said.

"You bet it's nice. Cost plenty, too. Yours looks like it's good for nothing but—"

"Swatting flies," Darrel said under his breath.

"What? Catching flies with that?"

"No. *Swatting* flies," Darrel said. "That's what I do in the barn every morning before school and every afternoon too."

The other boys snickered.

Steve gave Darrel a look that said, *Don't you dare try to make me look stupid again.* Darrel just smiled in return.

Later, after the gang had picked teams, Steve discovered that Darrel was on his side. "What position do you play?" Steve asked.

"Let me try shortstop," Darrel said.

"Look," Steve said, "you don't just start playing baseball at shortstop. You gotta start with something easier, like right field. You don't have any experience."

"Except for swatting those flies," Darrel said.

Steve gave him another dirty look.

Specs stepped in and said, "Darrel, why don't you head out to right field until you get the hang of the game."

"But I just want someone to give me a chance at short," he said.

"Later, Darrel," Specs said.

22

The game started with Specs at third base, Steve at first, and Darrel in right field. Darrel turned out to be a very bad hitter. The ball was always past him before he got the bat around. Steve snickered with every strike. Then, in the fifth inning, someone from the other team hit a ball to right field. Darrel was so bored that he wasn't paying attention, and the guy got a stand-up triple. Steve was no longer smiling. "You're a 98-pound weakling out there!" he yelled.

By the ninth inning, Steve's team was doing so badly that he decided to put Darrel at shortstop just for a laugh.

The first pitch was hit sharply right at Darrel. It looked as if it would get past him without his even trying for it, when suddenly Darrel snapped out his hand and snagged it. "See?" he said. "It's as easy as swatting flies."

Darrel was responsible for the final out, too. Again, he whipped out his hand at the last possible moment to grab the ball.

"I thought you hadn't played much baseball," Steve said later. "Where did you get the moves?"

"I practice in the barn twice a day," he replied. "I throw balls against the wall and swat at them with my flimsy glove like a cow swats at flies with her tail."

"I get it," Steve said, "swatting flies."

Later that evening, as he thought over the day's events, Specs remembered hearing something about weakness and strength in Sunday school.

With his parents' help, he found some Bible verses that helped him to understand that someone like Darrel who seems weak may also have some hidden strengths. Specs wrote the following passages down to share with his friends the next day:

Bible Clues: 2 Corinthians 12:9-10 and Romans 14:13.

Action idea: Try to think of someone who has more strengths than most people realize. What happens when you focus only on your weaknesses or the weaknesses of others? Thank God in prayer for the ways that God makes you strong.

Prayer time: Lord Jesus, I am weak but you are strong. But because you are strong and you are in me, I am also strong. Help me to share my weakness and your strength with others honestly. Amen.

The Truth about Toughies

Buddy had been called many things behind his back: Big Galoot, Meathead, and other worse things. But to his face he was always just "Buddy." Kids wanted to be on Buddy's good side because he could be pretty mean when he felt like it.

Everybody thought they had Buddy pegged. He was the big dummy. Every school had one, they thought.

But there was one thing about Buddy that had the other students guessing. Every Wednesday after school, Buddy was the first one out the door. He would bolt off in one direction or another at a fast clip. Once or twice, somebody had tried to follow him, but Buddy was too strong and too fast.

The four detectives, Erik, Specs, Brian, and Peter, saw this happen week after week and decided that this was a mystery they would have to solve, though they couldn't imagine what help Mrs. Gratz and her Bible would be on this one.

Specs devised a plan that was clearly brilliant. He even drew it out on some of his mother's fancy art paper which impressed the others and got them excited for the chase.

The following Wednesday, the four boys left school at the sound of the bell, mounted their bikes, and laid the trap. Each of them, from previous adventures, owned walkie-talkies. They carried these on their bikes to hiding places at the four points of the compass: Erik to the North, Specs to the South, Brian to the East, and Peter to the West.

They waited.

Brian broke the radio silence: "I've got him traveling East across Washington Street." Brian remained in hiding while the others peddled frantically in the three directions Buddy could have gone after he passed Brian.

Next, Peter spotted Buddy. "He's cutting between Kristy's house and the corner store. I don't think he suspects anything."

This continued as Buddy changed direction twice and even doubled back once on Erik. But the bikers kept with him. Finally, Specs announced with a note of triumph, "He's entering a building. It's the Nursing Home."

Cautiously, the boys took their places as sentries at the three entrances to the building. Since it was his plan, Specs volunteered to go in after Buddy.

Ten minutes later, he joined the other three just inside the front entrance and said, "We must have lost him."

Just then, they all heard a familiar voice. Even as they listened, the door to Room 115 opened and there was Buddy looking right at them and beginning to turn a dangerous color of red.

"Whacha doing here!" he yelled. He strode up and grabbed Peter by the collar. "Did you guys follow me?"

"Ah—ah—ah—" was all Peter could get out.

"Well, I don't want you telling about this or it will make me look bad."

Peter thought fast. "If you don't make a scene by knocking us around," he said, "there is no reason for anyone to know—whatever it is you don't want them to know."

Buddy looked thoughtfully at his right fist and at Peter's face. He flipped his thumb up and pointed with a sudden jerk to room 115. "That's my great-grandmother in there. She's 97 years old. I visit her sometimes."

The four boys looked at each other with surprise.

"It will be our secret," Erik said. Then he took Peter's collar from Buddy's hand and led the others outside.

Later, Mrs. Gratz listened to the "Saga of Big Buddy" and nodded. "People are never only good or only bad. We all have both sides to us. Once again, the Bible can give us some clues. Here boys, look these up:

"*Bible Clues:* Romans 2:14-15 and Romans 7:21-25."

Action idea: Think of something bad that you could do that you really wouldn't want your friends to find out about. Then think of a good thing you could do. Before reading any further, go do something as nice as Buddy did—if you dare!

Prayer time: Lord Jesus, I see now that there is nobody who is only good or only bad. Help me to resist the bad things I could do and do the good you wish for me, so that people may see that your presence in my life makes a difference. Amen.

The Story Continues

Erik slipped his feet over the edge of the bed, swiped at his hair with one hand, and looked at the clock.

"Nine o'clock!" he said with a start. "I'm late for school again." But presently his panic turned to a sinking feeling as he remembered. The funeral.

He dressed quietly in the suit his father had laid out the night before and spent some extra time wetting and combing his hair. Looking at himself in the mirror, he wondered how he would look crying. *Nobody looks good crying*, he decided, then he went downstairs.

"You look nice, dear," his mother said as he entered the kitchen. "We let you sleep late this morning."

"I noticed."

"Your uncle Bill got in late last night."

Erik brightened a bit. "Really?"

"He was wondering if you wanted to go with him to the reviewal."

"What's that?"

"That's where close family can go privately to see the body."

Erik saw a tear forming in his mother's eye. She turned away.

"Your father and I already went, but Karen didn't want to go." She waited for an answer. "It will be your last chance to see grandpa."

Grandpa, I already miss you, Erik thought. *We played games, we went fishing, you always had Lifesavers for me, and I never did beat you in the Story Game.*

"I'll go," Erik told his mother.

Erik and his uncle stood quietly at the edge of the casket, but Erik's head was crowded with thoughts: *It looks like grandpa is holding his breath; I wonder if Uncle Bill will touch him; I wonder how he feels since it was his father and only my grandfather; I'll just keep an eye on him— if he starts to cry I just know I'll fall apart.*

Bill stood in silence without any tears. After a while, he turned and winked at Erik, but the usual smirk was missing.

"Why did God do this?" Erik asked.

"What makes you think God is responsible?"

"Mrs. Robbins said God must have wanted grandpa more than we do."

"Nonsense."

"And the Johnsons said everything is God's will."

"Would the Johnsons say sin is God's will?"

"No, but—"

"Well, death is just part of the same brokenness as sin. It isn't God's will."

Once again, they looked down at grandpa in silence.

"Your grandpa and I used to play a game," Bill said. "We called it the Story Game."

"We played it, too," Erik replied. Bill turned and smiled at him.

"Then you know how it went. He started a story, I would add something really stupid, and he would have to work my part into his story."

"I never beat him at it," Erik said. "He was a fast thinker."

"I thought I had him once. Five minutes into the story, I had all the people in the world die. With no people, I thought there could be no further story."

"What happened?"

"He chuckled for a long time, then he said, ' "For God loved the world so much that he gave his only Son, so that everyone who believes in him may not die but have eternal life." ' "

"Then maybe grandpa's story is still going on."

"That's the point, Erik," Bill said. Then they cried together for a while but the tears were not bitter ones.

Erik received a sympathy card later that day. It was from Mrs. Gratz. It read:

> Sorry to hear about your grandfather, Erik. Death is a very great mystery, beyond figuring out in this life. But that does not mean we are without clues. May God bless you, my young friend.
>
> *Bible Clues:* Psalm 23:1-4; Matthew 16:18; and Romans 8:38-39.

Action idea: Write a letter or talk with someone who has recently lost a loved one. Ask them what they think of death. Think up a really hard question about death to ask your pastor. Then, ask.

Prayer time: Lord Jesus, it doesn't matter if I have been touched by a death close to me or not. Sooner or later, we are all touched by that darkness. What does matter is that I begin even now to trust that your story will never end. Amen.

Adopted?

"I think I was adopted."

"You've got to be kidding."

"I mean it, Erik," Peter said with feeling. "I have evidence."

"What evidence?"

"Well, for one thing, everybody in my family can roll their tongues and I can't. Don't you think that's strange?"

"Get serious," said Specs with a chuckle.

"OK. For another thing, everyone in my family has little hanging down parts on their ears that dangle. My little hanging down parts are hooked to my head."

"Those are called earlobes," Erik said. "Let me take a look—I guess you're right. Yours don't dangle."

"You have to have better evidence than that," Specs said.

"I'm the only one who isn't good at music, and I'm smaller than the rest of them, and—oh, there's lots of stuff."

Specs adjusted his glasses like he had something important to say. "Peter, all of that is what you call circumstantial evidence. What I mean is, it just *happens* that all those things are true— maybe."

"Have you talked with your parents about this?" asked Brian.

"No, I'm afraid of what they might say."

"There must be another way we can find out," Brian said.

"Sure, but how?"

"Have you ever seen your birth certificate?" Erik asked.

"I don't think so."

"Well, there you go," Erik said. "Why don't you just look around the house for your birth certificate and that ought to settle it for you."

"Hey, guys," Peter said meekly, "my parents are gone until suppertime. I don't suppose you want to go with me and look for that thing—"

"This could be it!" Peter exclaimed. "I remember seeing this metal box once before." Peter slid a gray box carefully out of his dad's closet, and they gathered around. Peter snapped open the lock and opened the box.

"Look," he said, "here's something that says 'Important Family Papers.' I don't think I could get in trouble for this; I'm family, aren't I?"

The others all nodded to reassure him, then glanced at the door as if they thought someone might walk in any moment.

"Here are our passports—we went to Germany last year— and here is something that says 'United States Army' on it. Here are some little blue slips with white writing. We've got it! Birth certificates. Here are mom's, dad's, Jason's, Melinda's— but nothing for me."

Peter sifted through the rest of the contents of the file swiftly and suddenly came upon a white envelope with a name on the outside: "Peter Alexander."

"Peter Alexander is me," Peter said softly. He opened the envelope with haste and found some official-looking papers inside. Peter read silently for about a minute and then said, "I don't understand all the words, but I know it means I was adopted." Peter slumped against the wall and said, "Oh, dear. Now I'm sorry I found out."

"Peter, maybe you're wrong," Erik said hopefully.

"Let's bring the papers to Mrs. Gratz and have her look at them," Brian said. "We'll have 'em back before your folks get home."

Peter looked up from the floor. "Good idea," he said.

"Peter, these papers do say that you were adopted," Mrs. Gratz said after reading a few pages. "I think you should talk with your parents as soon as possible. They can explain things. They should know that you know."

Peter was staring at the floor again.

"Does that bother you, Peter?"

"Yes. I don't belong anywhere now."

"Let me tell you a story, Peter. There was once a man who spent much of his time with outcasts, widows, and orphans. The so-called good people didn't like that. This man felt especially drawn to people who didn't have families."

"Like me?" Peter asked.

"No, Peter, you have a family. Yours is a family of one heart even though you may not share one blood. They want you and love you. This man took those who had families and those who didn't and made them into *one* family. After he died, this family spirit spread all the more."

"I know," Brian said. "You're talking about Jesus."

"Yes, I am. Peter, you may have lost your original family due to some tragedy, and maybe you were adopted. But you became a member of your present family because they loved you and *chose* you. Jesus did the same. Our sin makes us all orphans, broken away from our heavenly Father. But the Bible says that all who believe and are baptized are members of God's family. So, we are *all* adopted, aren't we?"

36

Mrs. Gratz looked around to see the effect her words would have. "Rather than being sad about it, doesn't it make you happy? And thankful? We were chosen!"

The boys all looked at Peter.

Peter looked at Mrs. Gratz, smiled, and then smiled some more.

Minutes later, they were trotting back to Peter's house with a slip that said:

"*Bible Clues:* Galatians 4:4-7 and Romans 8:14-17."

Action idea: Together with your family, plan a special meal to celebrate being together. Pray a special prayer of thanks to God for choosing all of us to be part of God's family.

Prayer time: Lord Jesus, I hear that we are all orphans because of our sinfulness. Thank you for not leaving us to find our own way in life; thank you for making us your sisters and brothers. Amen.

Camp Letters

Dear Mrs. Gratz,

Surprise! I bet you didn't expect to get a letter from me. The truth is, you won't be seeing any of us four detectives around town for a while because we are at Bible camp for two weeks—all except for Specs who doesn't belong to our church. But his parents say he can come with us next year if he wants to. (He's on vacation anyway.)

Everything is great here, except for one problem. All the guys have been a little lonely since we got here on Sunday, but two nights ago Brian started crying after supper. That wouldn't have been so bad, but after he went to see the camp nurse, two boys from another town made fun of him. Brian got mad and threw a softball at one of the kids and hit him in the leg. The leg swelled up pretty bad. The cabin counselor saw it happen, and now I think Brian is in trouble.

Brian refuses to apologize to the guy he hurt because he says he's mad. He won't even talk to us. He's too quiet at Bible studies, and he won't even go swimming with us. He just sits and watches from shore.

What I want to know is this. What can we do to help Brian join back up with the group? This is very important because things could get worse before they get better. Please write to me right away and tell me what we can do to solve this mystery.

> Yours truly,
> Erik

P.S. I would have called you long distance because this is so important, but I would have had to call collect and I figured I could explain things much better in a letter anyway.

P.S. #2 Please hurry. Thank you very much.

Dear Erik,

Thank you for your letter.

Tell Brian that I have another mystery for him alone to solve. Tell him to search for the shortest verse in the Bible. If he finds it, he will understand.

> Yours truly,
> Mrs. Gratz

P.S. I would have accepted a collect call from you, my friend.

P.S. #2 Please report back to me on what happens with Brian. Thank *you* very much!

Dear Mrs. Gratz,

Erik showed me your letter. I decided to answer it myself.

I looked all over the Bible and couldn't find a verse shorter than seven words. I don't think I found the right one because this is all I could find: "Worthless, wicked people go around telling lies." That one is from Proverbs 6:12, but I really don't think that you meant it for me (ha, ha!).

So, please write back to me before I leave camp to let me know what the shortest verse in the Bible really is.

While I was looking for this verse, I came across a few verses that helped me to get rid of some of my anger. In Acts, Chapter 2, for instance, I saw the question, "What shall we do, brothers?" I didn't know what to do either so I couldn't wait to see what the answer was. Peter's answer to the guys who asked him that question was, "Each one of you must turn away from his sins and be baptized in the name of Jesus Christ, so that your sins will be forgiven."

Well, I told the guy I hurt that I was sorry. But I have one problem. I have never been baptized. After finding this verse that tells how important

Baptism is, I went and talked to my counselor. He said that in some churches people are baptized when they're babies and in other churches they wait until they're older. The counselor said I should talk to my mom and dad and to my pastor when I get home. That sounds like a good idea to me!

So, even though I never found the shortest verse (I hope!), I did find some very good things in the Bible.

I haven't cried anymore since that first night, so the guys have quit bugging me. It was just embarrassing. That's all.

By the way, *what is* the shortest verse in the Bible?

Yours truly,
Brian

Dear Brian,

Bible Clues: "Jesus wept" (John 11:35). And, by the way, read Ephesians 4:26-27.

Yours faithfully,
Mrs. Gratz

Action idea: Think of at least two things you could do that would help a crying person not to feel stupid for crying. What would you do if your actions caused the person to cry in the first place?

42

Prayer time: Lord Jesus, why do I try to hide my emotions from you and the world when I know you see my true heart anyway? I'm glad the Bible says you cried. It makes you seem more real to me. Amen.

Caught in Between

"I'm so happy you boys can help me with my yard this summer," Mrs. Gratz said as she pushed the button for third floor.

The boys automatically looked up to watch the numbers.

"It's a good deal for us," said Erik. "We're too young to get real jobs anywhere else and you're paying us as good as anybody."

The others nodded in agreement. Mrs. Gratz stood at the door facing the boys—backwards for your average person on an elevator—but she didn't seem to notice or care.

"Since all four of you will be part of my Yard Guard, I need to get a couple of other garden tools so you each can have something to do. That's all on third floor."

Suddenly, the elevator simply halted in darkness. Everyone grabbed for a wall. There was a moment of stunned silence. Then, Mrs. Gratz started laughing with her low, raspy voice. One by one the boys started to giggle. It helped them not to be scared.

"Well," Mrs. Gratz said finally, "what do you suppose we do now?"

"Just wait, I guess," Specs said.

"Let's think of a way out of here," Peter suggested.

"I'll signal that we are in trouble," said Brian, and he pounded mightily on the door three times, then listened. He repeated this until they all heard a faint voice from somewhere below them: "Hang on, we'll have you out in a few minutes. Pound twice if you understand."

Brian pounded, then said, "*Now* we can sit and wait."

"Thank you, Brian," Mrs. Gratz said. "So, boys, are there any mysteries in your lives?" The murkiness was beginning to brighten.

"Nothing new, I guess, but I just kind of feel like a broken elevator myself," Specs said unexpectedly. "I feel like it's a crime or a disease to be 12 years old."

Mrs. Gratz laughed again and said, "What do you mean, Specs?"

"It's like I am caught between floors. I don't feel like a kid anymore, but I'm not a teenager either."

46

"I know what you mean," Erik said. "We're too old for kids' toys but we're too young to always get clothes for Christmas."

"Sounds like a serious case of the 'in-betweenies' to me," Mrs. Gratz said. "Everybody feels it at different times in their lives. This won't be the last time that you feel caught in between like this elevator."

"I think we've found our mystery," said Erik.

"Let's solve it together," Mrs. Gratz said. "What can we do about it?"

Silence.

"Let me ask you this question instead: What are we going to do about this elevator having the 'in-betweenies?' "

"Well, we just trust that someone is out there fixing it," Peter said.

"And so we wait," she replied. "But what if they don't get us out of here today, or this week, or this month?"

"They'll get us out before too long—I hope" Brian said. "We just gotta wait."

"So you're pretty hopeful, then, that this dark wait will be over soon."

"Sure."

"How about your case of the 'in-betweenies,' Specs?" Mrs. Gratz continued. "Do you think it's like the elevator? Will it be over soon?"

"I'm pretty sure I'll get out of this elevator before I get out of my 'in-betweenies,' " Specs replied. The others laughed. "But sure, I'll get over it," he added.

"Good! Then you are already doing something about it. You are *hoping*."

"Do you know any Bible verses that can help with this problem?" Erik asked. "I know the Bible doesn't talk about elevators and I don't think it says much about kids our age."

"Well," said Mrs. Gratz, "the Bible may not mention kids too often—not even much about Jesus at your age—but it does have many clues about waiting and hoping. For instance, you remember that Jesus was crucified on a Friday, Good Friday. He rose from the dead on Sunday, Easter Sunday. What do you think his followers were doing on the Saturday between those two days?"

"They *really* had the 'in-betweenies,' " Erik said.

"It was like being stuck in an elevator, only it was much darker than this," Mrs. Gratz replied. "Remind me to give you some special verses from Isaiah when we get back to my house."

The next thing they knew, the lights popped on brightly, causing them to shade their eyes. They heard a deep hum from far below, and the elevator once again continued its upward path.

Bible Clues: Luke 23:55—24:7 and Isaiah 40:30-31.

Action idea: Pray for people who are caught having to wait for something important to happen. Memorize at least one Bible verse that you think could help you while you wait.

Prayer time: Lord Jesus, being caught in between doesn't scare me so much if I know you're waiting for me. Amen.

Double-Dare

"I'm not afraid of anything."

"You keep telling us that, so why won't you join the club?"

Brian thought, *For such a pip-squeak, he sure is a big mouth.* Out loud he said, "I just am not interested, OK?"

"Well, we think you're scared, and if you are, we don't want you in the club anyway."

Brian stuck out his jaw and scowled at the other boys. *I could do what they ask,* he thought, *show them that I can pass their test, and then just not join the club. That would show them! I don't want to be a member of their lousy club.*

"So what's it gonna be?" Big Mouth asked.

"What do I have to do?"

The others laughed in a sly way, and the Big

Mouth said, "Meet us after school behind the gym."

"It's very simple," Big Mouth said. "You must do one thing to prove that you deserve to be a member of our group."

Brian looked from face to face and found that the others were enjoying his discomfort.

"One thing only. You must go into Alec's Market and steal one thing."

Brian curled his lip at the thought. *Is that all they want? And they make such a big deal of it.*

"But that one thing," Big Mouth continued, "is a *Playboy* magazine from behind the counter."

Brian's heart jumped a bit. *This is more serious,* he thought. *I'll need some kind of diversion.*

"Each of us has had to do it," the Big Mouth said. "We have eight great magazines. But you don't get to see any of them until you bring us your own. And another thing. None of us will help you."

"Somehow, that doesn't surprise me," Brian said, and he turned and headed for Alec's Market.

"Hey, Brian," Specs called as he jogged toward his friend. "Where are you going?"

"To Alec's Market."

"Great! You can buy me a soda."

Go away, Brian thought. *I've got to do this alone.*

"I'm kidding," Specs continued. "I know you're saving for the weight set. I hear you're even doing some babysitting to earn the bucks."

"Added to what Mrs. Gratz paid us for yard work, I'm doing pretty well," Brian said.

Brian felt the five dollar bill in his left front pocket and said, "But I will buy you a soda if you help me out with something."

"Name it," Specs said.

You are too trusting, my friend, thought Brian. Out loud he said, "My mother asked me to pick up a pound of hamburger, get a special package at the Post Office, and be back in 10 minutes. If you ask Mr. Cooper to package the meat for me and pick up the sodas, I could run over to the Post Office quickly and get home in time. What do you say?"

"Easy," said Specs. "I'll take the money."

When Specs entered the store, Brian pretended that he was going on to the Post Office, but instead he watched through the window as Specs talked with Mr. Cooper and then followed the market owner to the meat counter in the back of the store. As soon as they were out of sight, Brian carefully edged into the store, glanced down the aisles, slipped his hand behind the counter, and grabbed the first magazine he felt. With great relief, he found that he had gotten what he'd come for on the first try. He tucked the magazine into his shirt, glanced once again around the store, and stole quietly back out to the sidewalk.

He did not see the face of his buddy, Specs, watching his every move in a round mirror near the ceiling over the meat counter.

Outside, Specs found Brian walking toward him from the direction of the Post Office.

"The package isn't in, after all," Brian said. "Did you get what you went in there for?"

"Yes," Specs replied calmly. "Did you?"

Brian looked at him with wide eyes, but didn't get a chance to reply. Eight boys strode up to Brian wearing broad smiles. They winked, gave thumbs up, and patted Brian on the back. Big Mouth said, "You're one of us now."

Specs handed Brian the hamburger, the sodas, and the change, and said, "I've got to be going, Brian. Keep the soda."

Specs turned and began to walk away.

Brian took one look at Big Mouth's big grin, then called out, "Wait, Specs. Please wait."

Shoving past two of the club members, Brian walked back into the store, right up to Mr. Cooper at the front counter. "Sorry," Brian said as he pulled the magazine out of his shirt and handed it to Mr. Cooper.

Mr. Cooper acted as though people returned stolen merchandise every day and said, "That's quite all right." He winked at Brian and said, "Come again."

"I saw what you did back there," Specs said.

54

"I don't know why I did such a dumb thing," Brian replied.

"I don't know either—except those guys had some hold over you. But you showed them. It took real courage to stand up to eight of them like that. And then you actually walked back into the store and faced Mr. Cooper!"

"Well, as I always say, I'm not scared of anything—"

Specs laughed heartily. "Yeah," he said, "you *are* always saying that, aren't you?" He patted Brian on the back, popped open his can of soda, and added, "You could have gotten me in trouble with your fearless attitude, you know. I wonder what Mrs. Gratz would say about all this?"

"Brian, I'm glad you decided to return the magazine," Mrs. Gratz said later when the boys had told her of the afternoon's event. "I have some Bible clues to help you the next time you're faced with a decision like that:

"*Bible Clues:* 1 Timothy 6:20-21; 1 Corinthians 10:13; and Hebrews.2:18."

Action idea: On a piece of paper, write down the three areas where you are most often tempted to sin. Then write down as many ways that you can think of to fight those temptations.

Prayer time: Lord Jesus, I know that I sin against you, probably more often than I am even aware of. Forgive me. Help me to feel good about myself once again, and give me a chance to share forgiveness with others. Amen.

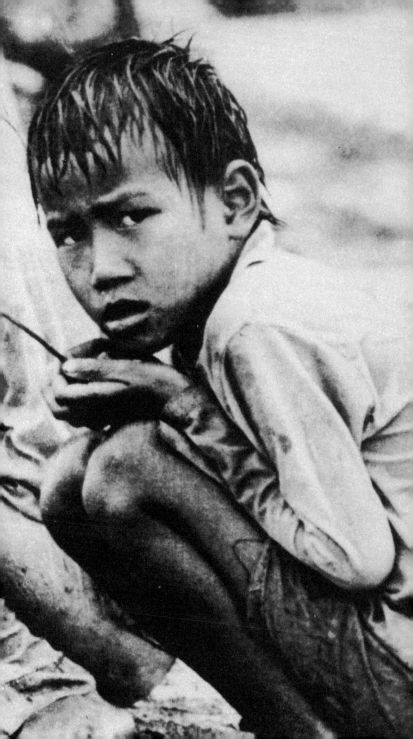

A Boy Named *Gwen*

"I want you all to be thinking of questions you want to ask *Gwen* when the interpreter gets here," Mrs. Docken said.

Every head in the class turned to look at the new Vietnamese refugee boy who had become a member of the class only last week. He was fiddling with his pencil, but suddenly realized that he was the center of attention. His head snapped up and he looked alertly from one face to another.

"So take a few minutes right now to write down some of your questions for the interpreter."

"Like, where did he get a girl's name," a voice snickered from the back of the room.

Those who heard it laughed along and Mrs. Docken cast them a dirty look. "You'd better keep your minds on your task," she said. "You only have a few minutes."

Soon, the bell rang for lunch. The class members threw their slips of paper with questions for Gwen on the teacher's desk on their way out of the room. Gwen waited until the last person had gone, then he followed slowly. Two girls were waiting for him halfway down the hall, and they escorted him to the lunch line.

"Hey Gwen," Billy said turning around to look at the boy, "it's just you and the other girls today, huh?" He sneered at Gwen and was met by a kind smile. "Go like this Gwen, nod your head like I do," Billy said.

Gwen looked at him and nodded his head.

"You like to play with dolls, don't you, and you'd really rather wear a dress, wouldn't you?"

Gwen looked at him again and nodded with him.

"That's enough, Billy," said Peter.

"He doesn't understand a word of it, so don't worry."

The kids moved along in the serving line.

"I hear you guys eat seaweed and fish heads," Billy said.

Gwen looked from face to face and saw that only Billy was smiling at the situation. He folded his arms in front of him, signaling that the game was over.

"You gotta watch out for those fish heads," Billy said. "Hold your nose when you eat those." And Billy reached for the boy's nose.

58

Gwen threw a hand up and slapped Billy's hand away before he could grab anything. Billy reached up with the other hand quickly, but that was slapped away too.

Billy made the mistake of trying to grab the boy's nose one more time, when suddenly Gwen swept his foot in an arch in front of him, catching Billy's legs and heaving him to the floor.

At this, many in the lunchroom turned to watch the commotion. Billy looked around with embarrassment and got to his feet.

"You don't kick me—" Billy started.

Gwen drew his right hand from his pocket and flicked open the blade of his pocket knife, then just as quickly closed it and returned it to his pocket. He looked nervously around and saw that many of the kids were backing away from him. Then he rattled off a phrase in Vietnamese and stepped forward to take a plate.

Peter fell in behind him and the others returned to the line after that.

Surprisingly, no teachers saw what had happened. And more surprisingly, apparently no one reported the incident to the principal.

Gwen and Peter ate their lunches in silence.

"Class, this is Mr. Van from Social Services. He has been in our country for many years and is going to ask Gwen some of the questions that you wrote out for him this morning."

59

"Before I ask him your questions, I think I will have him tell you some of his own story in his own way," Mr. Van said.

After a brief discussion with the interpreter, Gwen began to share his story through the interpreter. The class listened politely at first—except for Billy who made scraping noises under his chair—but the politeness turned to intrigue. The story that Gwen told was as unlikely as a fairy tale.

To begin with, his name was not Gwen, but *Nguyen*. He was named, not after a girl, but after a family of great kings. His escape from Vietnam bordered on the miraculous. His life was in danger many times: on the border crossing, on the old boat that took them to another land, and in the refugee camp where people struggled just to have enough to eat. During the boat trip, pirates attacked them 15 times. Valuable objects were taken and people were hurt. On the pirates' last visit to the boat, even the engine was taken, casting the refugees adrift in the middle of the ocean. They began to die in great numbers. Nguyen said, "The only good thing about all the dying was that the rest of us finally had room to stretch out on the cramped decks."

The question and answer period never took place. Everyone thought their questions would be too silly after they heard Nguyen's story.

After school, the boys and girls gathered around Nguyen and several invited him home for supper.

He didn't understand their words, but he sensed a difference in the way he was being treated. Even Billy came up and said, "See ya," before heading home.

Nguyen watched as Billy walked away, then he turned and winked at the others.

"He's even a Christian," Peter told Erik, Specs, and Brian later. The interpreter told me so after class. I guess that means that he worships the same God we do, doesn't he?"

"I don't know," Erik replied. "Let's ask Mrs. Gratz what the Bible says about all this."

Mrs. Gratz had these suggestions for them:

Bible Clues: Galatians 3:26-28; 1 Corinthians 1:10; and Matthew 28:19-20.

Action idea: Pretend, for just one hour, that you are from a foreign country and do not speak English. What are some things about our country that would be easy or hard to understand? What would you think about a Christian worship service?

Prayer time: Lord Jesus, it's easier sometimes to see how people are different from me than to see how we are alike. Help me to see people as you see them. Amen.

Between a Rock and a Wet Place

"If it starts to rain, don't go into a cave."

That would be the advice of Brian, Specs, Peter, and Erik nowadays—especially after their adventure in Riverside Park.

The boys were out for a walk. They discovered a stray black lab down by the river and were throwing sticks into the water so the dog would retrieve them. Then it started to rain.

"Come on," Erik said as he started to run, "I know where there's a cave."

They ran along the bank until they came to a bend in the river. Pointing to a path leading down the embankment from the main path, Erik said, "It's this way."

The boys slipped their way down the path as the rain began to pound even more heavily around them. They stepped around a narrow ledge of rock at the water's surface, then into the shelter of a large cave.

"Wow!" Specs said. "Look at the rock formations."

"This place must be as big as the school library," Peter said.

"I hear there is treasure buried in the sand floor," Brian said with a twinkle in his eye.

"The cave was formed by the force of the river through the years," Erik said.

Outside, the wind howled and began to sweep some of the heavy rain into the cave. The boys followed the dog, temporarily dubbed "Nightmare" for his dark coloring, up the gentle slope to the back of the cave and sat down with their backs against the sandstone wall.

An hour later, the boys were beginning to worry. The wind and rain hadn't let up at all, and the water of the river seemed to be rising. Water was beginning to lap over into the entrance of the cave. Specs found a piece of driftwood in the corner of the cave and stuck it in the sand at the point where the water was moving toward them. Within only 15 minutes, the stick was completely under water.

"I don't know about the rest of you," Specs said, "but I think somebody better go for help before the water covers the entrance completely." The four-foot opening was now more than half under water.

"But don't you think this will stop soon?" Erik asked.

"What if it doesn't?" Peter asked. "What if it gets worse?"

"It will be suppertime in a couple of hours," Specs said, "and people will start to look for us."

"But the entrance could be flooded by then," Erik said, "and it could take them all night or even a week to find us here. *Why* did I bring us here!"

"I would go," Brian said, "but I can't swim too well."

In the end, it was Peter who volunteered. That surprised everyone—Peter was usually the one who was afraid. "After all," he explained, "I am the strongest swimmer of the group, and even though I am afraid, I am even more afraid to stay here."

The others escorted Peter through the waist deep water to the entrance of the cave. Outside, they could hardly see more than a few feet through the wind and the rain. The boys tied their shirts together in square knots and tied the line around Peter's chest. With wishes of good luck, he was off.

Clinging to the slippery rock in the rain and fierce wind, Peter never really had a chance. Just seconds after leaving the cave entrance, he lost his grip on the stone face and the shirt pulled away from his chest.

The last glimpse the others had was of Peter coming to the surface and beginning to stroke mightily in the water as he was swept around the bend and into the wall of rain.

"It was stupid!" Erik exclaimed. "We never should have let him do it."

"What do we do now?" Specs yelled above the roar.

"Peter will make it," Brian said calmly, but inside he was very worried.

"The only thing we can do now," Erik said, "is wait. By the time we could get help to Peter, it would be way too late. And we won't help ourselves by putting ourselves in any more danger." Erik started to cry and the boys all helped each other back up the slope to join the dog.

Less than an hour later, the water had risen until the entire entrance was covered. The water lapped close to where the boys sat. The cave was so dark they couldn't see where the water level was. They could only guess by the *lap, lap* of the waves.

"Dear Jesus, we don't know how long we have been waiting here in this black cave," Erik said out loud. They held onto each others' shoulders for support. "It seems like the sun should have been up hours ago. The thing is, Jesus, we're scared. The water is still rising. We think there may be a gap in the ceiling of the cave because it just isn't trapping the air like it should." Erik paused. "What else should I say?"

"Just talk with him like it's a conversation," Brian said. "That's what our Sunday school teacher says to do."

"Keep it up, you're doing fine," Specs added.

"We especially want you to help Peter, and let our parents know we're still all right—for a while. Bring someone to help us. Please."

"You did good, Erik," Brian said. "Amen."

"That's the first time I ever prayed out loud, except for the table prayer, the goodnight prayer, and the Lord's Prayer."

"Nothing like a little tragedy to help someone learn to pray," Specs said. He held the dog higher to clear the water.

Another piece of time that felt like an hour passed.

The high water had long since blocked out the sound of the storm, so the sudden bubbling and churning near the entrance of the cave sounded loud and dangerous to the boys. Then, a splash.

"Hello in there," a voice came.

You will not understand what the boys felt in their hearts until you go through something equally dark. They were, for lack of a better word, jubilant.

The scuba diver explained that Peter had shown them where the boys were. It took so long because the flood waters had changed the landscape.

One by one, the boys trusted the diver to lead them under the water to see a bright sunrise on the other side.

Outside, Peter hugged each of them while the news reporters shot pictures that would appear on the front page of many newspapers. Peter became a celebrity and a hero for throwing himself into a flood to save his friends.

When a magazine ran their story a few months later, it closed with a quote from Peter: "My life will never be the same after this. I learned to pray—and I hear my friends did too. We learned the hard way what the Bible has been teaching all along!"

Sometime later, the boys received a note in the mail from Mrs. Gratz. It read:

"Bible Clues: Philippians 4:6-7; Matthew 6:7-13; and Romans 8:26-27.*"*

Action idea: You don't have to get caught in a cave to learn how to pray. Take some time now to have a conversation with God. Share with God (silently or aloud) the ups and downs of your life. Once you can do this, your life will never be the same.

Prayer time: Lord Jesus, I don't want to have to go through a tragedy before I learn how to pray better. Teach me now. Amen.

Innies and Outies

"Life is like a bellybutton," Brian said with a serious air.

The others looked at each other as though Brian had just gone off the deep end.

"I'll bite," Erik said. "Tell us, Brian, how is life like a bellybutton."

"I'm glad you asked me that question. I've been waiting all day for someone to ask me that question."

"Knock it off and tell us," Peter said, bunching his fist up in a mock warning.

"Life is like a bellybutton because there are only two kinds of people and two kinds of bellybuttons: Innies and Outies. Laugh at me if you want, but it's true." Brian sat back against the tree and enjoyed the puzzled expressions on the faces of his three friends.

"Bellybuttons, I understand," Peter said, "but life is a much harder thing. Please tell us more of this, oh great and wise one."

"Well," Brian said, enjoying the attention, "there are more Innies than Outies among the world's supply of bellybuttons. But there are a lot more Outies than Innies, I think, where people are concerned. Think of all the things that you can't join or be a part of for one reason or another."

"What do you mean?" Erik asked.

"For instance," Brian continued, "I can't be a member of Big Mouth's club unless I steal a dirty magazine."

"I can't be a member of the honor role Specs and Erik are on in school unless I get my grades up," Peter said.

"I can no longer be in the Drive-In's Birthday Club," Erik said, "now that I've turned 12."

"The swimming team discriminates against those of us who sink rather than swim," Brian said.

"To vote, you've got to be 18," Specs said.

"You've even got to be in a wheelchair to be on the YMCA's wheelchair basketball team," Peter said. "That excludes us all."

"Yes, but think of all the things that people in wheelchairs are excluded from," Erik said. "They can't go into the basement of our church for a wedding reception without someone's help, they can't visit many houses easily, they don't fit in some bathrooms, and lots of other things. I wouldn't know about this except that my cousin

70

has muscular dystrophy and is in a wheelchair most of the time."

"There are a lot of Outies, just like I said," Brian replied. "I think we ought to start a club that doesn't exclude anyone."

The others thought it was a good idea, so they went over to Mrs. Gratz's house to have her help write up a charter for their new club.

"It's a wonderful idea," she said.

"We wondered if you could help us come up with some rules and guidelines," Brian said. "You know—official stuff."

"What you need is a charter," Mrs. Gratz replied.

"You've got it!" Brian said.

"I have just the thing," she said, "in final form, too."

"You've got to be kidding," Erik said. "Have you been looking in your crystal ball again to know what we would ask you?"

"No," she chuckled, "I've been reading my Bible again. Now *there* is a charter for you. There's lots of official stuff in it."

It dawned on Peter first.

"I get it," he said. "I know what we could call the club that doesn't make Outies of people."

"What?" Brian asked.

"It already has a name, doesn't it, Mrs. Gratz?" Peter asked.

"That it does, Peter," she replied.

"Well, what is it?" the others asked impatiently.

"The church!" Peter said with triumph.

"Jesus Christ died for all people—to make all people Innies—" Mrs. Gratz said, "unless they absolutely insist on starting their own club and not inviting Jesus to be a member."

"Now," Brian said, "what can we do about the bellybutton situation?"

"What!" Mrs. Gratz said with surprise in her voice.

"Mrs. Gratz," he continued, "what did God do with the extra bellybuttons?"

He looked at her startled expression.

"He put them in the naval reserve," Brian concluded.

"Oh, my," Mrs. Gratz said.

The other boys booed, then they all laughed merrily.

"Since I can't find bellybuttons in the Bible," she continued, "I'll have to find you some really good passages on the church. Let's start with these:

"*Bible Clues:* Colossians 1:18-20; 1 Corinthians 14:12; and 1 Corinthians 12:12-13."

Action idea: Enlist someone in God's club—the church—by inviting someone along to a youth event or to Sunday school.

Prayer time: Lord Jesus, deep in my heart when I think about you, I want to be a member of your church more than any other group. Thank you for making that possible. Amen.

Secret Thoughts about Church

"You guys are going to think I'm crazy," Peter said.

"The last two times we thought that, you thought you were adopted—which turned out to be true, and you volunteered to risk going for help when we were stuck in the cave—which saved our lives," Erik said. "With a record like that, I'm not going to be the first to call you crazy."

"Well," Peter continued, "I really like searching out all these mysteries with Mrs. Gratz—"

"That's not crazy; we all do," Specs said.

"—but I honestly don't like going to church that well."

"Again, nobody is going to call you crazy," Brian said. "It can get pretty boring sometimes."

"Here comes the crazy part," Peter said. "Sometimes in the middle of a church service I get the strangest urge to stand up and yell."

Brian tried to stifle a laugh, but he snorted anyway.

"I know. I'm crazy," Peter sighed.

"Not so fast here," Specs said. "I practice archery at my church—in my head anyway. I imagine myself shooting all kinds of things when the service seems especially boring."

"I like to draw," Erik said. "If it's a good sermon, I sketch what the pastor is talking about. But if it is boring, I draw anything that comes to mind."

"Well, if it is getting to be confession time," Brian said, "I guess I could say I do some strange things during some worship services. I say the alphabet forwards and backwards really fast and time it on the stopwatch part of my watch. My record is nine seconds."

"Are you kidding? You can do that?" Peter asked with raised eyebrows.

"Time me: ABCDEFGHIJKLMNOPQRSTU VWXYZZYXWVUTSRQPONMLKJIHGF EDCBA."

"Wow!" Peter exclaimed. "Ten seconds."

"And I can hold my breath for over a minute and a half, but the trick is to let my breath out at the end without gasping."

"Peter, I was right," Erik said. "You're not crazy. Brian is the crazy one."

"Hey, I'm not that bad all the time," Brian said in his own defense. "Most of the time I really like the music and other things."

"Like the children's sermon?" Peter asked.

"Sure," Brian said. "I'm not afraid to admit that. I get a lot out of those things for the kids, if you want to know the truth."

"I like it when the pastor tells stories as part of his sermon," Erik said. "And special music is nice."

"We like all the special touches in a church service," Brian said. "None of us is crazy for wanting worship to be good."

"I wonder what we can do to help the services be as good as they can be?" Peter asked. "Let's go talk to Mrs. Gratz. She always has some good ideas."

Later the boys left Mrs. Gratz's house with these verses:

Bible Clues: Romans 12:1 and Psalm 95:1-7.

Action idea: Talk to your pastor about the possibility of your helping with a worship service. If you aren't comfortable with that, at least take a friend or two with you to share some thoughts on worship with your pastor and even the worship committee, if possible. Get into the habit of telling your pastor and other worship leaders when they do something that you especially like. It is more likely to happen again.

Prayer time: Dear God, give your church leaders a deep faith so that when we all worship together we may see you more clearly. Amen.

A Surprising Book

Dear Boys,

I am going to be out of town for a couple of weeks, so instead of our getting together to search for clues from the Bible, I thought I would write you all a letter about my favorite book, the source of our fine clues, God's written Word.

Did you know that there have been more copies of the Bible printed than any other book? We're not the only ones to treasure it.

It is a large book, larger than it even looks because it is usually printed on such thin paper. In fact, with almost 800,000 words, it is equal in size to about 25 of the usual books you read.

But just because it is large doesn't mean it is boring. Some people are scared away by its size and never try reading it. Anyone who says it's all boring hasn't read the Bible! To prove it to you, I will list a handful of things that I found in the Bible in recent months since meeting you boys. You won't believe what I have found!

1. An army of 700 left-handed men, each of whom could "sling a stone at a strand of hair and never miss" (Judges 20:16).

2. A man who lived to be 969 years old! (Genesis 5:27).

3. A donkey who lost his temper and said, "What have I done to you? Why have you beaten me these three times?" (Numbers 22:28).

4. The sun stood still for a day during a battle! (Joshua 10:13).

5. Hezekiah lived for 15 extra years because he prayed (Isaiah 38:4-6).

6. A graveyard full of dead bones was brought back to life! (Ezekiel 37:10).

7. And the greatest and strangest thing of all that you will find in the Bible is how God came down to earth in the form of a human being. We weren't understanding God's message and will very well, so God sent Jesus to make sure we understood how much we are loved. (You can read about this all over the New Testament.)

So, you can see that this book of clues has some fascinating things in it. There is enough for you to explore for a lifetime.

Keep up the good work you are doing with mysteries and Bible clues. Are there any more mysteries out there or have you solved them all? Here are a couple more Bible clues. Happy searching!

Bible Clues: Isaiah 55:10-11; and 2 Peter 1:21.
Your Friend in Jesus,
Mrs. Gratz

Action idea: Ask someone special what his or her favorite verse in the Bible is. Then write that verse on a piece of construction paper in your fanciest writing and add some personal touches by drawing some pictures or pasting some artwork on the sheet. Give it to the person as a gift.

Prayer time: Lord Jesus, you are the living Word. I thank you that in the written Word, the Bible, I can meet you in a special way and know that your life is in me. Amen.

In League with God

"Hey, what's wrong with Darrel?" Specs asked. "I just asked him if he was going to the youth group's swim this weekend and he nearly bit me in half with his answer."

"I haven't seen him at a youth event for a few months," Erik said. "In fact, I haven't seen him around at all except during classes."

"Well, I don't like having someone shoot his mouth off at me when I never did him any wrong," Specs said.

"Just leave him be," Brian said. "Anyone who acts like that can just sit in it. He's got to live with himself; that's punishment enough."

"But it just isn't like him," Specs said. "He and I are a lot alike, or at least we used to be. I can't just quit being his friend."

"Then maybe Darrel has to be our next mystery," suggested Erik.

"I'd like that," Specs said with a note of relief.

"Seems to me like the easiest way to attack this mystery is just to go up to Darrel and ask him what's going on," Brian suggested.

"We'll have to do it without Peter," Erik said. "He was an hour late for school this morning and didn't have a written excuse, so he's helping stuff envelopes in the secretary's office until 5:00."

"Let's go find Darrel, then," Specs said.

They caught up with Darrel at the bike rack before he headed for home.

"What's up, Darrel?" Specs asked.

"Gotta go do chores," he replied.

"We were wondering why you aren't going swimming—" Brian began, but he was cut short.

"I told Specs I don't like your stupid youth group stuff, so leave me alone, OK? And I'm not going to church anymore," Darrel snapped. With that, he peddled out so fast that he kicked gravel out behind him, hitting Specs in the hand.

"Ouch! That's the end of that, then."

Peter walked up to join them. "Hey, I saw that," he said. "What's his problem?"

"Doesn't matter," Specs replied. "Let's go."

"I don't get it," Peter said. "He said he had to go do chores, but I happen to know that he is living with his mother here in town now."

"What?" Erik asked.

"I overheard the secretary on the phone just a few minutes ago. She took a call from a social worker who said that Darrel's address should now be listed as being here in town. The secretary turned to a teacher afterwards and said, 'Too bad, I hear they have to split the farm up for the divorce settlement.'"

"Let's talk with Darrel once more tomorrow," Specs said. "He's worth it."

"Yeah, the farm's gotta go." Darrel said later. "I don't know what dad's going to do then. But if they don't split the farm, then mom's got no money or support. Everything is tied up in the farm."

Specs, Erik, Brian, and Peter stood quietly, not knowing what to say.

"That old farm has been in the family for a long time, and it's partly my fault that the family can't make it."

"How do you mean?" Specs asked.

"If I had only been a better kid, done my work without complaining so much, stayed at home more instead of going out so much—"

"You work harder than all four of us put together," Brian said firmly.

"It's not good enough, though," Darrel said. "I still fall short. I could have done better. Then maybe mom and dad wouldn't have split up."

"Come with us," Specs said. "We want you to meet someone."

"Yes, you probably did fall short," Mrs. Gratz told Darrel.

"That's what I like about her," Erik whispered to Brian. "She doesn't pull a punch. But I know she also has something hopeful to say."

"The Bible says that we all fall short in God's eyes—you included," Mrs. Gratz continued.

"That's not very hopeful," Brian whispered back.

"Just wait," Erik replied.

"But God doesn't expect us to be perfect," she said as she looked deep into Darrel's eyes. "God *does* ask us to follow the two great commandments."

"I thought there were 10," Darrel said.

"There are, but Jesus gave us two on which all others depend: 'Love the Lord your God with all your heart, with all your soul, and with all your mind,' and 'Love your neighbor *as you love yourself.*' "

Darrel sat in silence.

"I sense that your parents taught you quite well how to love God and how to love your neighbor, Darrel," Mrs. Gratz said, "but God also tells us to do all that *'as you love yourself.'* This divorce may not help you to think better of yourself, but be assured that to God you are still of great worth. And it's not your fault that your parents divorced."

"What did I tell you?" Erik whispered as he nudged Brian. "She knows how to give a guy hope."

"Am I worth as much as these guys?" Darrel asked with a tight mouth and dancing eyes.

84

"Absolutely," Mrs. Gratz answered. "I can convince you with some Bible clues."

"Then I guess I could climb into the same pool with them."

"If you don't get thrown in first," Specs said.

Bible Clues: Matthew 10:29-31; and Genesis 1:26-31.

Action idea: Think of two ways you could communicate that someone is of worth without saying or writing the message. Many kids whose parents go through divorce think they are to blame more than is probably true. How could *you* convince Darrel that the divorce was not his fault?

Prayer time: Lord Jesus, if we are all worth so much to you that you would die for us, then I think I will treat others better—and myself too! Amen.

Banana Beer on Trial

Erik, Brian, and Peter looked down the tables at the many treasures brought from Africa by the missionary. Cowhide sandals, heavily beaded jewelry, long knives in wooden sheathes covered with taut leather, a cowhorn instrument, a sweeping fur headdress, spears and shields, a Swahili Bible, and other various things.

Brian absentmindedly picked up a large bowl-like gourd with a stick for a handle.

"Guess what that is," a voice said from behind him. Brian turned to see the missionary who had just addressed the Sunday school.

"A mixing bowl," Brian answered.

"It's an enormous beer mug," the man said. "They use it for their *pombe* (pōm–bay)."

"They have beer over there?" Peter asked.

"Alcohol is all over the world in many forms,"

the missionary replied. "The East Africans drink *pombe*, banana beer."

"Can they get drunk on it?" Erik asked.

"They say that on the first day *pombe* is as mild as soda pop, on the second day it is like a light beer, on the third it is like a strong wine, on the fourth it is as powerful as whiskey, and on the fifth it will eat a hole in the bottom of the bucket. Boys your age drink it all the time."

"Really?" Peter said.

"Of course, some of them get married around your age, too," the missionary said with a smile.

"I wonder what the Bible says about drinking *pombe*," Erik said. "Do you preach against it?"

"That's not as easy a question as you might think," the man replied. "Which of you can remember what Jesus' first miracle was?"

Erik knew because he had been reading in the book of John just recently, but he didn't want the others to think he was a know-it-all with the Bible, so he remained silent.

"In John, Chapter 2, Jesus turned about 150 gallons of water into wine," the missionary said. "So, I'm not against all alcohol because I don't think the Bible is against all alcohol. On the other hand, I am against broken families and people losing their jobs and their health due to drinking. That, too, happens all over the world."

"It happens here, too," Erik said.

"Have you boys been offered beer or anything yet?"

Only Peter shook his head no. The others motioned yes.

"I figured so," the missionary said. "It gets younger and younger every time I get back to the States. But I want you to remember something, a story. When I was growing up in Madagascar, I remember walking along a path with some schoolmates of mine. We saw a brightly-beaded snake sunning itself along the base of a building. Someone said 'Let's catch it,' so we circled it and moved in on it—I made sure I was on the tail end of the thing because I really don't like snakes. Anyway, we moved in on it. 'Step on it if it comes toward you,' another voice said. You might guess that the serpent would come at the one who is most scared—me. I couldn't show fear to my friends, so I stepped on it. It coiled itself around my ankle and started crawling *up the inside of my blue jeans.* Needless to say, I screamed and kicked until the thing went flying. One of the other boys said, 'I wonder if it was a coral snake or a sand snake.' Being new to the country, I said, 'Oh, do they look alike?' 'Yes,' he replied, 'but only one of them is poisonous.' Here comes the punch line. Alcohol is like that snake. We begin by toying with it and making sport of it, but suddenly some of us find alcohol coiling itself around our lives and putting us in danger."

Brian put the *pombe* bowl down. "This thing is more deadly than even your spears, I think," he said.

89

"Neither of them are deadly by themselves," the missionary replied. "People make them that way sometimes. The Bible goes into detail on this. I have some verses I want you to read."

Bible Clues: John 2:1-11; and Proverbs 23:29-32.

Action idea: Do some of your friends drink? Does someone you know have a drinking problem? Think of a way you could help that person. Or enlist the help of an adult who could talk to the person. Check out a book from the library on the subject of alcoholism.

Prayer time: Lord Jesus, help me to make good choices about important things like the use of alcohol. Keep me from hurting myself. Amen.

It Takes One to Know One

"I can't believe I lost," Specs said as he looked at the chart on the front bulletin board of the public library. "I read all summer long, sometimes a book a day, in order to win this reading contest."

"What was the prize for winning?" Peter asked.

"No prize, just knowing that I read more books than anyone else this summer."

"Your prize actually was what you got out of reading the books," Peter said, "—that is, if you actually read them."

"You bet I did," Specs said as he took his glasses off to clean them with his shirt. "But I wonder if Jeremy read them all."

"It's all on the honor system. There's no way we could find out now," said Peter.

"Maybe, and maybe not," Specs said.

Specs walked up to the circulation desk and asked the librarian, "Is it a secret what books Jeremy read to win the summer reading contest?"

"Not at all," he replied. "Would you like to see the list? I have it right here, and I assure you they aren't a bunch of easy books, if that's what you were wondering."

Specs made a photocopy of the list, then proceded to find as many of them as possible and stack them on a back table.

"Look here," Specs told Peter after checking inside the front covers and taking notes. "Fifteen of these books were all checked out at one time just two weeks ago."

"How do you know that Jeremy didn't read them all?" Peter asked.

"I don't," was the reply, "but I can find out."

His method was not flashy, but it was effective. Specs simply asked Jeremy's little sister a few questions after school the next day.

"Oh, sure, I can tell you what Jeremy has been doing the last couple of weeks just before school started," she said. "He was out at the lake up north. We were all on vacation."

"Was Jeremy reading a lot during the vacation?" Specs asked. Just then, Jeremy came around the corner, spotted his sister talking with the boys, so he came over.

"Hey, sis," he said, "we can't afford to miss the bus today. Mom wants us home by 4:00."

"I forgot," she said. "I'll meet you out there."

"All right, he replied. "Hi, Specs. Hi, Peter. Bye, Specs. Bye, Peter." And he was gone. His sister put on her jacket.

"Like I was saying," Specs said, looking again at Jeremy's sister, "was Jeremy reading a lot during the vacation?"

"You're silly," she answered. "He was just here and you could have asked him yourself." Then she ran off down the hall.

"So close," Peter said. "But what do you care if he cheated or not? So what if he did?"

"I would know, that's all."

"Know what?"

"That he's a cheater."

"I don't have to stake out a library and grill a guy's sister to know that he sometimes cheats," Peter said. "We all do that sometimes, even though we don't like to admit it. I'll bet I could even find a Bible verse that says that."

"Do it and I'll drop my investigation right here," Specs challenged.

Peter spent the evening looking up key words in the concordance in the back of his Bible, and in the morning he presented Specs with three Bible passages:

Bible Clues: Romans 3:10-12; Romans 3:23; and John 8:7.

Action idea: The next time you are at a campfire, hold a stick tightly in your hand. Have it represent one particular sin that God shows you. Squeeze that stick as though you hate it, then throw it in the fire. You may not be able to name every sin you have ever done, but you can ask God to let that one confessed sin stand for all the others too. After you have done that, look up 1 John 1:8-9.

Prayer time: Lord Jesus, I only have to look in the mirror to find a sinner. Forgive me and all who trust in you for salvation. Amen.

Lover Boy

"I'm in love, Mrs. Gratz, and I can't talk with anybody else about it. You've got to help me."

"You've been smitten, Erik."

"Smitten? What does that mean?"

"It's a wonderful word. Look it up in the dictionary."

"I will. I'll look it up the next time I'm in the library, but I won't be able to even read the words, because *she* works there."

"Who?" Mrs. Gratz asked.

"Miss Morgan, the assistant librarian," Erik said boldly.

"Oh, my," Mrs. Gratz said, "an older woman."

"Not so old," he replied. "She's working her way through college. She is twenty years old—almost a teenager."

"And you are how old?"

"Twelve," Erik said.

"Almost a teenager," she said with an understanding nod.

"She's beautiful," he said. "Am I so screwed up in my thinking?"

"No, Erik, not you. I can tell that you're serious—and I believe that you are experiencing a kind of love."

"Oh, thank you for saying that. I was afraid nobody would believe me—but what do I do?"

"About what?"

"About my feelings."

"Enjoy them. There are many people who would pay riches to feel love as you feel it now," Mrs. Gratz said.

"I'd sell them any day. This isn't fun, you know."

"Fun is too simple a word for love. There is so much more to love, depending on what kind it is."

"You mean there is more than one kind of love?" Erik asked.

"In English, we have only the one word," she said. "But in the language of the Bible there are several. There is a sexual love—which will make more sense to you later. There is a family type of love. There is a friendship kind of love. And there is a high and godly kind of love. Your feelings for Miss Morgan might be a combination of these."

"You are probably right. None of those categories seems to fit exactly."

"Don't be afraid of love, Erik," Mrs. Gratz said. "It is your God who made you able to feel what you feel. Read what God's Word has to say about love.

"Bible Clues: 1 John 4:7-8; 1 Corinthians 13:4-7; and John 15:9."

Action idea: Give somebody a kiss or a hug today. Tell someone in your family that you love him or her. Write a note to someone telling the person how much he or she means to you. Mention your love for God in a prayer before you go to bed tonight.

Prayer time: Dear Jesus, you are the Lord of love, and if anyone can teach me about love, it is you. Teach me. Amen.

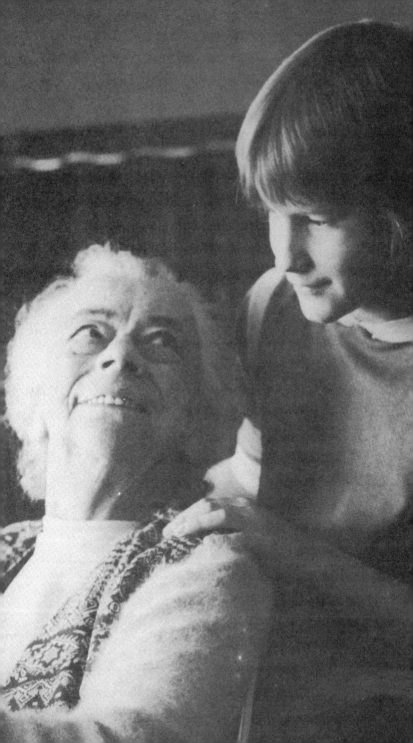

Wishes and Other Prayers

The boys browsed quietly through the musty books in Mrs. Gratz's Reading Room.

So much that she could be reading, Erik thought, *yet she seems to read only her Bible.*

In the corner of the room, a small writing desk sat surrounded by two walls of pictures. Some looked older than Mrs. Gratz herself. Others were recent snapshots.

Funny, I've never thought to ask her about her family—why she lives alone or whether she has relatives near here, Erik thought. *We've all been too interested in our mysteries.*

Some clattering in the hallway announced their hostess. Brian jumped to open the door, and Mrs. Gratz entered carrying a silver tray with cookies and five small glasses of milk.

"This brings back memories of the night we first met," she said. "It was a night like this, but I don't think we'll have scratching at the window this time," she chuckled.

"I wish we could have met you another way," Erik said.

"But I don't get out that often," Mrs. Gratz said, "so the chances of that would have been slight. I think you were sent to me that night."

"You do?" Specs asked from the biggest and stuffiest sitting chair.

"Sure. I had been wishing for something new in my life. The days were all becoming a bit too gray and alike for my tastes."

"Well, you have certainly spiced up our lives, too," Peter said. "We've never had so many adventures and mysteries."

"We've all had wishes come true," Brian said.

"You mean we had *prayers* come true," Peter said.

"What's the difference?" Brian asked.

"Is there a difference?" asked Specs.

"Let's try a little exercise," Mrs. Gratz suggested, "but you must eat while I talk. Assume for just a moment that I really was the mysterious woman with the crystal ball that you thought I was. And then imagine that when you came here that first night I offered you each one wish that could come true. What would you have wished for?"

"Three more wishes," Erik answered quickly.

"Besides that," she said.

Nobody answered quickly this time.

"You don't have to tell me your wish," she said, "but as you think about what it might have been, ask yourself if you could have asked for it in the name of Jesus."

Erik nodded his head. "I wish you really *could* make our wishes come true."

"I don't have the power to do that, but as a believer I do have the power to lift them up to God with you. I can help you turn your wishes into prayers by pointing you to the Lord Jesus. And he wants to give you the desire of your heart."

"Jesus will say yes to anything we ask for?" Peter asked.

"I didn't say that," Mrs. Gratz replied. "He wants to answer your prayer, but sometimes the answer is 'No' or 'Wait.' "

"But he answers everything?" Brian asked.

"If the name of Jesus can be attached to it, as we should always pray, then it will be answered," she said.

"Then I can go around and change the world just by what I pray," Erik said.

"Even if you have faith the size of a mustard seed," she replied. "But the prayers are likely to have an even larger effect on the one who prays."

Mrs. Gratz leaned forward to reach for a slip of paper. "I must have known we were going to

101

talk about prayer today because I already wrote down a few verses that you can look up."

But just as her fingers reached the paper, she slid off the couch in slow motion and crumpled up on the floor.

The paper read:

"*Bible Clues:* John 14:12-14; Matthew 7:8; 2 Corinthians 12:8-9."

Action idea: Why do you suppose Paul's prayer to have the "thorn in the flesh" (2 Corinthians 12:7) removed from him was never answered? Or was it answered? Think of at least two of your prayers that were answered, but not in the way that you requested.

Prayer time: Lord Jesus, you have promised to hear us when we pray. That makes me feel like I need never be alone. I think I will pray more often! Amen.

Intensive Caring

"I'm truly sorry," the nurse said. "Nobody but family is allowed in there, and then only for 10 minutes at a time."

"Just ask her," Brian said with as much sweetness in his husky voice as he could muster.

The nurse looked at the faces of the persistent boys. "Well," she said, "as long as you are the ones who rode here in the ambulance, I'll ask the doctor if you can see her."

The nurse went down the hall.

"Did they say it was heart attack or stroke or what?" Peter asked.

"Nobody is saying anything yet," Erik answered.

"Do you think we should tell our folks we are here?" Specs asked.

"I already called mine," Brian answered, "so we can have a ride home in a bit."

The nurse returned.

"You have 10 minutes," she said, "but no more. She *must* have some rest." The nurse softened. "Besides, I really think it would do her wonders to have you boys in there, so let's call it part of her therapy."

They walked very slowly into the darkened room, their eyes adjusting to the soft light.

The boys were mildly shocked to see Mrs. Gratz hooked up to tubes and monitors as she was.

"It's my turn to have a mystery, boys," their friend said in a weak but steady voice. "How did I get to this hospital?"

"We called an ambulance," Peter said.

"It's a good thing you boys were there," she said. "A good thing."

"We only have a few minutes with you," Erik said with misty eyes. "Can we pray with you?"

"Yes, you can," she replied, "and yes, you may."

"Erik," Brian said, "you did such a good job in the cave, why don't you lead us again."

"But I don't know what to say—"

"Just talk to God, remember?" Specs said.

"All right," he said.

Mrs. Gratz reached up and took Brian's and Peter's hands; they joined with Erik and Specs until the circle was unbroken.

"Dear Jesus," Erik began, "I think I am praying in your will and your name when I pray for Mrs. Gratz to get better. We pray that she not only get a little better, but that she find the most perfect healing you can give her. She has given us so much; now we want to give her this gift of prayer. I don't know what else to say—except—thank you for hearing us. Amen."

"Come back tomorrow," Mrs. Gratz said. "I'll make sure they let you in. Don't worry about me. Go now, and God bless you."

Erik called the hospital first thing in the morning, but the nurse would not give out any information on the phone. So Erik called the others and they caught a ride to the hospital with Erik's father who was on his way to work.

"I'm sorry," the nurse said quietly, "Mrs. Gratz expired in the night."

"What does that mean?" Peter asked in his smallest voice.

"She died at 3:00 A.M. this morning. I'm sorry."

The boys were stunned.

"Is there any family here?" Erik asked.

"There is no family," the nurse replied.

"Have you notified anyone of her death?" he asked back.

"She didn't give us any names when she was questioned last night. You boys have been her only visitors."

"Can we do anything—you know—to help?" Brian asked.

"We have already asked Sunset Funeral Home to take care of things. You may want to call them," the nurse said. "Oh, by the way, she left this cassette tape for you. One of our aids lent her a tape recorder last night after you boys left. I don't know what is on the tape; I left the room to give her some privacy."

Erik took the tape. "Thank you," he managed to say from his choked throat, and his eye caught these words written on the cassette's label:

"*Bible Clue:* Genesis 27:2-4."

Action idea: Don't do anything. Sometimes when we hurt we need to just wait for some of the hurt to pass. The friends of Job came to be with him in his pain, and the first thing they did was to sit with him in silence for seven days and seven nights (Job 2:13).

Prayer time: Lord Jesus, help me not to avoid times that are difficult. I won't go looking for those times, but I know that you will be with me when they come upon me. Amen.

The Most Perfect Healing

"Hello, boys.

"I am recording this message to you now because I don't think I will make it through the night. I'm not one to pretend things are good when they aren't, so I'm telling you this up front. If I do hang on for a while, I'll just keep this cassette around until the day when I finally go to be with my Lord. So, you will get this eventually, anyway.

"There are so many things I wish I could tell you. There is so much you have to learn—though I must say that you are all unusually wise for your age. But I don't have time to go through any more mysteries *with* you. In fact, I think I'll go through the next one alone. I've always wondered what it would feel like to die. I think mine won't be so painful. I'm going ahead to investigate. You will all join me in your own time.

"In the meantime, there are many more mysteries to bring to God's Word. And there are many more *people* to bring to God's Word. Now that you have found out how fun the Bible is—no, 'fun' is too simple a word for God's Word just as it is for love. Now that you have discovered a place for God's Word in your life, can you imagine being without it? And yet many people don't have what you boys have, a love for searching out the truths of the universe. Tell them. Or better yet, *show* them.

"I want to give you boys a gift. Let's call it a lesson in God's grace. Grace means something that is given to a person even though the person may not have earned it.

"You boys came into my life by trespassing on my property, scratching my back wall with your ladder, and chewing up my back garden when you all fell. I laugh now when I remember that. But I was mad at first. If you hadn't come in for milk and cookies, I certainly would have had the police nab you.

"You were all so eager to discover God's Word that I forgot my anger and learned to love each of you very much. Erik, you are a leader in your quiet way; may you lead others to Christ. Specs, you are a scholar; dig deeply into the mysteries of God and share your insights. Brian, you are fearless; share the gospel with the courage of the

Apostles. Peter, you are the meek one of the group, but remember, 'Meekness is not weakness, but velvet-covered steel.'

"My gift to you boys has in one way long since been given. I see that you have caught something of my terrific love for God's Word.

"But now, as a reminder of that greater gift of God, I choose to leave everything I own to be equally divided among you four boys. My lawyer will inform you of the details. Finally, you will discover whether or not it is true that I am rich. But in another way, you already know.

"My final Bible clue for you is one that I can recite by heart:

. . . I remind you to keep alive the gift that God gave you when I laid my hands on you. For the Spirit that God has given us does not make us timid; instead, his Spirit fills us with power, love, and self-control.

Do not be ashamed, then, of witnessing for our Lord; neither be ashamed of me, a prisoner for Christ's sake. Instead, take your part in suffering for the Good News, as God gives you the strength for it. He saved us and called us to be his own people, not because of what we have done, but because of his own purpose and grace. He gave us this grace by means of Christ Jesus before the beginning of time, but now it has been revealed to us through the coming of our Savior, Christ

Jesus. He has ended the power of death and through the gospel has revealed immortal life.

"That is from 2 Timothy 1:6-10.

"God bless you all, my friends. Erik, I believe that the 'most perfect healing' that you asked God to give me is to go to be with God. Thank you for that prayer. Keep searching the Bible and solving the little mysteries in your lives. Good-bye my friends. I love you all."